KS1 SATs
Reading
10-Minute Tests

Rachel Lopiccolo

Schofield&Sims

Introduction

This book contains 22 bite-sized tests to give you practice in answering comprehension questions quickly. Each test contains a fiction, non-fiction or poetry text followed by between five and six questions and is designed to be completed in 10 minutes. The questions are just like the questions you will need to answer in the SATs Reading paper in Year 2.

What you will need

- a pencil
- an eraser
- a clock, watch or stopwatch
- an adult to time you and mark the tests for you

How to use the book

Make sure that you are sitting in a quiet place where there aren't any distractions. Turn to **Test 1** on page 4. When you are ready to begin, ask the adult to start the timer. Read the text and then answer the questions.

Work through the questions in order. Try to answer every question. If you get stuck on a question, leave it and move on to the next one. Work quickly and try to do your best. Remember, this is not a memory test. You can – and should – refer to the text as often as you need to answer the questions.

When you reach the end of the test, stop and tell the adult that you have finished. The adult will mark your test. Then the adult will fill in the **Total marks** and **Time taken** sections at the end of the test.

Turn to the **Progress chart** on page 48. Write your score in the box and colour the chart to show this score. If you got some of the questions wrong, have another go at them before you look at the answers. Then ask the adult to check your work and help if you are still not sure.

Published by **Schofield & Sims Ltd**, 7 Mariner Court, Wakefield, West Yorkshire WF4 3FL, UK
Telephone 01484 607080
www.schofieldandsims.co.uk

This edition copyright © Schofield & Sims Ltd, 2019
First published in 2019
Second impression 2020

Author: **Rachel Lopiccolo**
Rachel Lopiccolo has asserted her moral rights under the Copyright, Designs and Patents Act, 1988, to be identified as the author of this work.

British Library Cataloguing in Publication Data
A catalogue record for this book is available from the British Library.

What do you do on a nature walk? copyright © Kate Williams and used with permission. Extract from pages 7–9 of **Mr Majeika** by Humphrey Carpenter published by Puffin. Copyright © Humphrey Carpenter, 1984.

Extract from **The Colour of Home** by Mary Hoffman published by Frances Lincoln Ltd, copyright © 2002. Reproduced by permission of Frances Lincoln Ltd, an imprint of the Quarto Group. Extract from **Fantastic Mr Fox** by Roald Dahl © The Roald Dahl Story Company Limited. Published by Penguin Books Limited and used with permission. Extract from **Sky the Unwanted Kitten** by Holly Webb. Reproduced by permission of Stripes Publishing Limited. Text copyright © Holly Webb, 2008. Extract from pages 122–124 of **The Sheep-Pig** by Dick King-Smith published by Puffin. Copyright © Dick King-Smith, 1999. Reproduced by permission of Penguin Books Ltd. Extract from pages 1–2 of **Nim's Island** by Wendy Orr published by Puffin. Copyright © Wendy Orr, 1999. Reproduced by permission of Penguin Books Ltd. Extract from **The Fox and the Ghost King** by Michael Morpurgo. Published by HarperCollins and used with permission. Extract from **The Otter Who Wanted To Know** by Jill Tomlinson. Text copyright © 1979 Jill Tomlinson. Published by Egmont UK Limited and used with permission. **The Fly** by Walter Ramal. Reproduced by permission of The Literary Trustees of Walter de la Mare and The Society of Authors as their representative.

Design by **Ledgard Jepson**
Illustration by **Tamara Joubert (Beehive Illustration)**
Printed in the UK by **Page Bros (Norwich) Ltd**

ISBN 978 07217 1498 1

Contents

Notes for parents, teachers and other adult helpers

A pull-out answers section (pages A1 to A8) appears in the centre of this book, between pages 24 and 25. This provides answers to all the questions, along with guidance on marking the papers. Remove the pull-out section before the child begins working through the tests.

Test 1

'**What do you do on a nature walk?**'

We have an adventure, that's what –
Crunching through the undergrowth,
Dodging thorns and stings,
Leaping logs and bridging bogs,
Looking out for things:
Birds and frogs and shy hedgehogs
And flies with fairy wings,
And slimy slugs and tiny bugs –
Whatever nature brings!

Kate Williams

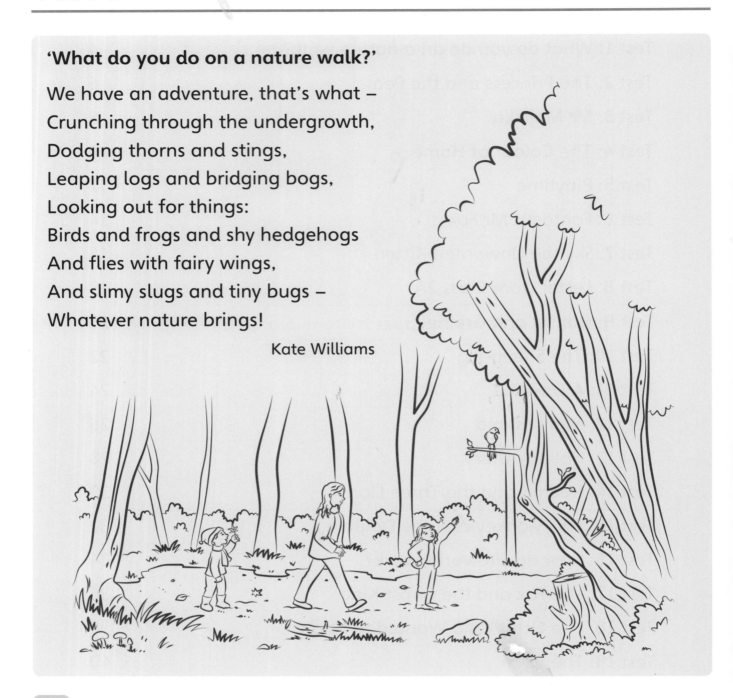

1 **Find** and **copy one** word from the poem that describes the sound of footsteps on the walk.

crunching

1 mark

2 Write down **two** things that the poet says you can do on a nature walk.

1) dodging thorns and stings

2) flies with fairy wings

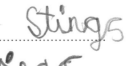

1 mark

3 Draw **three** lines to match the creature to the description used in the poem.

flies		tiny
slugs		with fairy wings
bugs		slimy

1 mark

4 Which **two** things does the poet try to avoid on a nature walk?

1) .....Jaws and.....

2) .....Stings.....

1 mark

5 How do you think the poet feels about going on a nature walk? Tick **one**.

It's scary. ☐   It's boring. ☐

It's tiring. ☐   It's fun. ☑

1 mark

6 Why do you think the poet describes hedgehogs as *shy*? Tick **one**.

They are slow. ☐   They are prickly. ☐

They like to hide. ☑   They are small. ☐

1 mark

Total marks .....5½/2.....   Time taken .....

'The Princess and the Pea'

Long ago, there was a prince who wanted to marry a princess. A *real* princess. There were no real princesses in the country where he lived, so the prince decided to travel the world. He met many princesses on his journey, but he could never tell if they really were *real* princesses.

He returned home to his castle feeling sad. What point was there in having a beautiful castle and all this land to look upon without a princess to share it with?

But then, one evening, there was a terrible storm: lightning flashed, thunder crashed and rain fell in torrents. As the prince watched the storm from his window, he heard a knock at the door.

A young lady stood on the doorstep. She said she was a princess in need of shelter from the storm, but she didn't look much like a princess; she was soaked to the skin, her clothes were dirty and wet and her hair was sodden and out of place.

The prince did not know whether to believe that the young lady was a princess, but he had a plan. That evening, he placed a pea on the bed that she would sleep on. He then laid twenty mattresses on top of it. She would have to lie on the pea all night.

In the morning, the prince asked the young lady how she had slept.

"I couldn't sleep at all!" she cried. "There was something hard in that bed. I feel bruised all over."

The prince was delighted. Only a real princess would feel a pea through all those mattresses. At last he had found his real princess.

1   What is the weather like when the princess arrives at the castle?
    Tick **one**.

    frosty ☐   sunny ☐   stormy ☑   foggy ☐

    ☑
    1 mark

2   How many mattresses does the prince put on the princess's bed?

    20

    ☑
    1 mark

3   Why does the prince put a pea under the mattresses?

    So he nos if it is
    a princess

    ☑
    1 mark

4   How does the prince find out that the young lady is a real princess?
    Tick **one**.

    She told him she was a princess.   ☐

    She slept all night.   ☐

    She could not feel the pea through the mattresses.   ☐

    She could feel the pea through the mattresses.   ☑

    ☑
    1 mark

5   What do you think will happen next in the story?

    get maried

    Explain why.

    because he is a
    prince and she is a princess

    ☑
    2 marks

    Total marks   5/5   Time taken

Test 3

Extract from *Mr Majeika* by Humphrey Carpenter

It is the first day back at school after the Christmas holidays. Mr Potter, the head teacher, is not happy because Class Three's new teacher has not arrived.

Mr Potter was still fiddling with the folding doors, so he didn't see what was happening. But Class Three did.

One of the big windows in the classroom slid open all by itself, and *something* flew in.

It was a man on a magic carpet.

There could be no doubt about that. Class Three knew a magic carpet when they saw one. After all, they'd read *Aladdin* and all that sort of stuff. There are magic carpets all over the place in *Aladdin*. But this wasn't *Aladdin*. This was St Barty's Primary School on a wet Monday morning. And magic carpets don't turn up in schools. Class Three knew that. So they stared.

The carpet hung in the air for a moment, as if it wasn't sure what to do. Then it came down on the floor with a bump. 'Ow!' said the man sitting on it.

He was quite old, and he had a pointed beard and very bright eyes, behind a pair of glasses. His hair and clothes were wet from the rain. On the whole he looked quite ordinary – except for the fact that he was sitting on a magic carpet.

'I just can't manage it,' said Mr Potter, still pushing at the folding doors. 'I'll have to go and get the caretaker.'

Then he saw the man on the carpet.

'What – how – eh?' said Mr Potter.

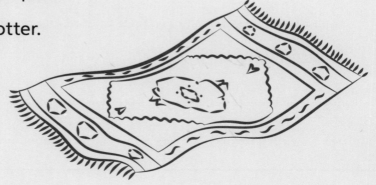

1 Number these events from 1 to 4 to show the order in which they happen in the story.

A man on a magic carpet flies into the classroom.	2
Mr Potter notices the man.	4
The window opens by itself.	1
The carpet lands on the floor with a bump.	3

✓ 1 mark

2 On what day of the week is the story set?

First day back after the christmas holidays

✓ 1 mark

3 Why does Mr Potter not realise that the magic carpet has flown in through the window? Tick **one**.

He is busy marking books. ☐

He is busy working with a group of children. ☐

He is busy trying to mend the doors. ☑

He is busy reading *Aladdin*. ☐

✓ 1 mark

4 How does Mr Potter feel when he sees the man on the carpet?

shoced

✓ 1 mark

5 List **three** things about the appearance of the man on the carpet.

1) long pointy beard

2) regular man

3) old man

3

✓ 3 marks

Total marks 7   Time taken 5 minits

Extract from *The Colour of Home* by Mary Hoffman

"We have a new boy joining us at school today," said Miss Kelly. "He's called Hassan and he's from Somalia. I want you to make him feel at home."

But the classroom didn't feel like home to Hassan at all. In his real home he had lessons out of doors from early morning until the sun got too hot at midday. Here he had to stay indoors except in the middle of the day, when he shivered outside in the damp playground.

The children were friendly. They smiled at Hassan and one of the boys kicked a football towards him. But he didn't understand anything that anyone said – only his name and 'hello' and 'toilet'. It was tiring remembering even a few English words.

After lunch, which Hassan didn't eat because he didn't know what it was, Miss Kelly gave all the children big sheets of gritty grey paper and pinned them to easels. She gave Hassan paintbrushes and a pot of water and showed him where all the colours were. He understood from her smiles and movements that she wanted him to paint a picture, but he had never done such a thing before.

He watched the children for a while, then chose a bottle of bright blue.

He painted a blue, blue sky, without any clouds. Then a white house, a yellow sun and mimosa trees. Outside the house, he made stick figures – himself, his father, his mother holding a bundle that was his baby sister, his grandparents, his uncle, his two cousins. There were nine people outside the house, who all lived inside it.

1 Which country does Hassan come from?

Somalia

1 mark

2 **Find** and **copy one** word that shows that Hassan is cold at lunchtime.

damp

1 mark

3 Which **three** words does Hassan understand?

1) *Hassan*

2) *hello*

3) *toilet*

1 mark

4 Why do you think Hassan *watched the children for a while* before starting his painting? Tick **one**.

He didn't know what to do. ☐

He was hungry. ☐

He was waiting for the blue paint. ☑

He wanted to go outside and play football. ☐

1 mark

5 How can you tell that Hassan has not lived in England for very long? Give **two** ways.

1) *he dosont no English*

2) *it did not fell like home*

2 marks

Total marks .... Time taken ....

Test 5

'Playtime'

Why do we have to go out to play?
It's cold, it's windy, it's wet!
Why do we have to go out to play?
Can't we practise the alphabet?
Why do we have to go out to play?
The weatherman said it might snow.
Why do we have to go out to play?
We like it indoors, you know!
Why do we have to go out to play?
There's nothing out there to do!
Why do we have to go out to play?
We prefer it inside with you.
Why do we have to go out to play?
The thought of it fills us with dread!
Why do we have to go out to play?
Oh, there goes the bell for lessons …
… Can't we go out to play now instead?

1   **Find** and **copy one** word from the poem that means the same as *damp*.

wet

1 mark

2   Which **four** types of weather are mentioned in the poem?

1) cold

2) windy

3) wet

4) snow

1 mark

3 What do the children want to practise instead of going out to play?

Tick **one**.

maths ☐   reading ☐

the alphabet ☑   playing the recorder ☐

☑
1 mark

---

4 *The thought of it fills us with dread!*

This means that the thought of going out to play makes the children feel:

Tick **one**.

hungry ☐   angry ☐

worried ☑   excited ☐

☑
1 mark

---

5 Who said it might snow?

the children

☑
1 mark

---

6 Why do you think the children want to go out to play at the end of the poem?

because it

☑
1 mark

Total marks 6   Time taken 5

Test 6

Extract from *Fantastic Mr Fox* by Roald Dahl

Mr Fox needs to feed his family and friends, but his access to food has been foiled by three cruel farmers who are keeping watch over his hole. After several days underground, Mr Fox comes up with a plan to burrow into the three farms to find food and drink. This extract is taken from the end of the book, where the animals are feasting on the stolen food.

The table was covered with chickens and ducks and geese and hams and bacon, and everyone was tucking into the lovely food.

"My darling!" cried Mrs Fox, jumping up and hugging Mr Fox. "We couldn't wait! Please forgive us!" Then she hugged the Smallest Fox of all, and Mrs Badger hugged Badger, and everyone hugged everyone else. Amid shouts of joy, the great jars of cider were placed upon the table, and Mr Fox and Badger and the Smallest Fox sat down with the others.

You must remember that no one had eaten a thing for several days. They were ravenous. So for a while, there was no conversation at all. There was only the sound of crunching and chewing as the animals attacked the succulent food.

At last, Badger stood up. He raised his glass of cider and called out, "A toast! I want you all to stand and drink a toast to our dear friend who has saved our lives this day – Mr Fox!"

"To Mr Fox!" they all shouted, standing up and raising their glasses. "To Mr Fox! Long may he live!"

Then Mrs Fox got shyly to her feet and said, "I don't want to make a speech. I just want to say one thing, and it is this: MY HUSBAND IS A FANTASTIC FOX." Everyone clapped and cheered.

succulent = juicy and delicious

1 What are the animals drinking?

....

1 mark

---

2 Why are the animals toasting Mr Fox? Tick **one**.

It is his birthday. ☐   He gave a speech. ☐

He is a fantastic fox. ☐   He saved their lives. ☐

☐
1 mark

---

3 Look at the paragraph starting *You must remember that no one had eaten a thing for several days*. **Find** and **copy one** word that describes how hungry the animals are.

....

☐
1 mark

---

4 Draw **three** lines to match the characters to what they do in the story.

Mrs Fox	•	•	makes a toast
Badger	•	•	eat without talking
All the animals	•	•	hugs the Smallest Fox of all

☐
1 mark

---

5 How do you think the animals are feeling? Tick **one**.

angry ☐   upset ☐   happy ☐   worried ☐

How do you know?

....

....

☐
2 marks

Total marks ....   Time taken ....

Test **7**

Extract from *Sky the Unwanted Kitten* by Holly Webb

Lucy gulped. It was obvious that Sky didn't know what was going on. She crouched down by her basket. "Mum and Dad are right," she whispered to the kitten, running one finger down Sky's back. "You do deserve a better home than this. I've come to say goodbye," she murmured, her eyes filling with tears. One of them dripped onto Sky's nose, making her jump.

"Mrow!" she mewed indignantly, and Lucy laughed and cried at the same time, stifling the strange noise in case her parents heard. Sky's face was so funny, her blue eyes round and cross.

"Ssshh, Sky!" Lucy scooped Sky up, tucking her into her dressing gown. "Come on," she whispered. Lucy looked around quickly as she opened the kitchen door, then scurried up the stairs to her room.

Sky snuggled against Lucy's pyjamas, watching curiously as they went upstairs. She'd never got this far before, the stairs were steep and someone always caught her before she'd struggled up more than a few steps.

Where was she going? Sky purred excitedly as Lucy opened the door to her room and placed her down gently on the floor.

Lucy snuggled under her duvet and watched Sky exploring her bedroom, sniffing her way around the boxes. Having Sky in her room made the little kitten seem much more *hers*, somehow. Lucy could imagine doing her homework up here, with Sky sitting on her windowsill watching the birds, or snoozing on her duvet. Sky clambered onto the bed next to Lucy and purred lovingly in her ear.

"What am I going to do, Sky?"

indignantly = crossly

---

1   Look at the first paragraph.
    Find and **copy two** words that describe how Lucy talks to Sky.

    1) ....

    2) ....

2 Why do you think Lucy is crying at the start of the text?

....

....

1 mark

3 In the text, Lucy *scurried up the stairs to her room*. This means that she went up the stairs … Tick **one**.

quickly ☐   slowly ☐   loudly ☐   angrily ☐

1 mark

4 *Sky snuggled against Lucy's pyjamas,* **watching curiously** *as they went upstairs.* Why is Sky *watching curiously*? Tick **one**.

because she is scared about where Lucy is taking her ☐

because she has never been upstairs and wonders what it will be like ☐

because she thinks she will be fed ☐

because she has never seen Lucy before ☐

1 mark

5 Look at the paragraph beginning *Where was she going?* How can you tell that Sky is happy about being in Lucy's room?

....

1 mark

6 What does Lucy imagine Sky will do while she does her homework? Tick **two**.

sit on the windowsill ☐   snooze on the duvet ☐

sleep in a basket ☐   sit on her homework ☐

1 mark

Total marks ....   Time taken ....

Test 8

Ms Liverpool (Head teacher)
Little Piper Primary School
Cherry Blossom Lane
Pipertown
PP8 1EC

Class 2A
Little Piper Primary School
Cherry Blossom Lane
Pipertown
PP8 1EC

24th October 2019

Dear Ms Liverpool

We are writing to ask you if we can get a school pet. We have been discussing it in class and we think that there are lots of very good reasons for getting one.

We think that a pet would help everyone in the school to feel happier. Pets are brought into hospitals and care homes to help patients and residents feel better, so we think it would be worthwhile to have a pet in school. It would also help to teach everyone in school to be more caring and responsible.

Some other schools nearby have school pets and the children and teachers there say that this has helped to reduce their stress levels. Animals have a soothing effect on people, especially during busy or difficult times, and we think our school would benefit from having one too.

We have thought about the different types of pet we could get. For example, a cat could help to catch the mice that live in the store cupboard or, if you would prefer an animal that could live outside, we could get a sheep to help keep the grass on the school field short. This would save money as the school would no longer need to pay for a gardener.

We hope that you like our idea and will consider agreeing to our request.

Yours sincerely,

The pupils in Class 2A

---

1   Who has written the letter? Tick **one**.

children ☐   the head teacher ☐

parents ☐   a doctor in a hospital ☐

☐

1 mark

2 What is Ms Liverpool's job?

....

1 mark

3 What reasons do the letter writers give for wanting to get a school pet? Tick **three**.

Stress levels would be reduced. ☐

Pets are cute. ☐

The teachers want a pet. ☐

Everyone in school would feel happier. ☐

It would teach pupils about responsibility. ☐

☐
1 mark

4 Which **three** places do the letter writers mention as allowing pets?

1) ....

2) ....

3) ....

☐
1 mark

5 What reason do the letter writers give for getting each of these animals?

Animal	Reason
Cat	....
Sheep	....

☐
2 marks

Total marks .... Time taken ....

Test 9

Extract from 'Hansel and Grethel'

Hansel and Grethel are the children of a poor woodcutter, whose wicked wife has decided to take them into the forest and leave them there. However, Hansel suspects that his stepmother is up to something and devises a plan to keep him and his sister safe.

As soon as it was quiet, Hansel got up, put on his little coat, unfastened the door, and slipped out. The moon shone brightly, and the white pebble stones which lay before the cottage door glistened like new silver money. Hansel stooped and picked up as many of the white pebbles as he could stuff into his little coat pockets. He then went back to Grethel and said, "Be comforted, dear little sister, and sleep in peace; heaven will take care of us." Then he laid himself down again in bed, and slept till the day broke.

As soon as the sun was risen, the stepmother came and woke the two children, and said, "Get up, you lazy bones, and come into the wood with me to gather wood for the fire." Then she gave each of them a piece of bread, and said, "You must keep that to eat for your dinner, and don't quarrel over it, for you will get nothing more."

Grethel took the bread under her charge, for Hansel's pockets were full of pebbles. Then the stepmother led them a long way into the forest. They had gone but a very short distance when Hansel looked back at the house, and this he did again and again.

1 How do we know that it is night-time at the start of the story?

....

1 mark

2 What *glistened like new silver money?*

Tick **one**.

wood ☐   bread ☐   pebbles ☐   the moon ☐   ☐

1 mark

3 Why does Hansel go outside during the night?

....

1 mark

4 Look at the paragraph starting *As soon as the sun was risen...*

Find and **copy one** word that means the same as *argue*.

....   ☐

1 mark

5 How can we tell that the stepmother is unkind towards Hansel and Grethel?

Mention **two** ways.

1) ....

2) ....   ☐

2 marks

Total marks ....   Time taken ....

Test 10

Extract from *The Sheep-Pig* by Dick King-Smith

Babe, a young pig, discovers that he can herd sheep just by asking them nicely. Farmer Hogget, noticing Babe's abilities, trains the pig to work as a sheep-dog and enters him into the sheep-dog trials at the county show. Mrs Hogget is watching the competition at home on TV.

As Mrs Hogget and hundreds of thousands of other viewers looked, they saw Fly go trotting back towards the car park.

And from it, cantering through the never-ending rain, came the long, lean, beautifully clean figure of a Large White pig.

Straight to Hogget's side ran Babe, and stood like a statue, his great ears fanned, his little eyes fixed upon the distant sheep.

At home, Mrs Hogget's mouth opened wide, but for once no sound came from it.

On the course, there was a moment of stunned silence and then a great burst of noise.

On the screen, cameras showed every aspect of the amazing scene – the spectators pointing, gaping, grinning; the red-faced judges hastily conferring; Hogget and Babe waiting patiently; and finally the commentator.

"This is really quite ridiculous," he said with a shamefaced smile, "but in point of fact there seems to be nothing in the rule book that says that only sheep-dogs may compete. So it looks as though the judges are bound to allow Mr Hogget to run this, er, sheep-pig I suppose we'll have to call it, ha ha! One look at it, and the sheep will disappear into the next county without a doubt! Still, we might as well end the day with a good laugh!"

---

1 What is the weather like in the story? Tick **one**.

dry ☐   sunny ☐   wet ☐   windy ☐

☐

1 mark

---

2 Look at the second paragraph.
Find and **copy one** word that describes how Babe moves.

....

☐

1 mark

---

3 *...Mrs Hogget's mouth opened wide, but for once no sound came from it.* What does this suggest about Mrs Hogget? Tick **one**.

She is surprised. ☐   She is angry. ☐

She is happy. ☐   She is scared. ☐

☐

1 mark

---

4 Draw **three** lines to match each character to their response.

| the spectators | • | • | waiting patiently |

| the judges | • | • | conferring |

| Mr Hogget and Babe | • | • | pointing, gaping and grinning |

☐

1 mark

---

5 **Find** and **copy one** word that means the same as <u>vanish</u>.

....

☐

1 mark

---

6 What does the commentator think will happen next?

....

☐

1 mark

Total marks ....   Time taken ....

Test 11

'A Day Out'

Once upon a time,
Not very long ago,
I took a train to York,
All on my very own.

I wandered round the city walls,
I visited York Minster,
I drank a coffee, ate a cake,
And felt so pleased to be there.

The day was very cold,
The sky as grey as slate,
But I didn't really care,
Because it felt like an escape.

I climbed the steps to Clifford's Tower
And walked along the river,
But as the day came to an end,
I soon began to shiver.

I strolled back to the station
And jumped aboard the train,
But I knew inside my heart,
I would be back again.

KS1 SATs Reading 10-Minute Tests

Notes for parents, teachers and other adult helpers

KS1 SATs Reading 10-Minute Tests are short, timed tests designed to build speed and confidence.

The questions in the tests closely match the questions children will need to answer in the Key Stage 1 SATs Reading paper, which is taken in Year 2. As children work through the book, the tests get progressively more challenging.

It is intended that children will take around 10 minutes to complete each test.

How to use the book

Remove this pull-out section before giving the book to the child.

Before the child begins work on the first test, together read the instructions on page 2. As you do so, point out to the child that there is a target time of 10 minutes for completing the test.

Make sure the child has all the equipment in the list headed **What you will need** on page 2.

Be sure that the child knows to tell you clearly when they have finished the test.

When the child is ready, say 'Start the test now' and make a note of the start time.

When the child has finished, make a note of the end time and then work out how long they took to complete the test. Then fill in the **Time taken** section, which appears at the end of the test.

Mark the child's answers using this pull-out section. Each test is out of six marks. Most questions are worth 1 mark. For questions worth 2 marks, follow the advice on whether to award 0, 1 or 2 marks. No half marks can be awarded. Then complete the **Total marks** section at the end of the test.

Turn to the **Progress chart** on page 48. Encourage the child to write their score in the box and colour the chart to show this score.

Whatever the test score, always encourage the child to have another go at the questions that they got wrong – without looking at the answers. If the child's answers are still incorrect, work through these questions together.

If the child struggles with particular question types, help them to develop the strategies needed.

Ask them to complete the next test at a later date, once they have had sufficient time to practise any question types they found difficult.

For questions requiring longer written answers, examples of possible answers children may give are provided. Often, multiple answers are possible so the examples are not exhaustive. Providing your child has given a sensible suggestion and fulfilled the criteria for the question, they should be awarded the mark/s.

Answers

Test 1 (page 4)

1 crunching   **1 mark**

2 **Award 1 mark for any two of the following:**
- have an adventure
- crunch through the undergrowth
- dodge thorns (and/or stings)
- leap logs
- bridge bogs
- look out for things

3 **Award 1 mark for all three lines drawn correctly:**

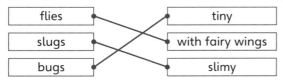

flies	tiny
slugs	with fairy wings
bugs	slimy

4 **Award 1 mark for both correct:**
thorns and stings

5 It's fun.   **1 mark**

6 They like to hide.   **1 mark**

Test 2 (page 6)

1 stormy   **1 mark**

2 twenty   **1 mark**

3 to find out if she is a real princess (because only a real princess would feel a pea through twenty mattresses)   **1 mark**

4 She could feel the pea through the mattresses.   **1 mark**

5 **Award 1 mark for a sensible prediction (various answers possible).** For example:
- They will live happily ever after.
- The prince will ask the princess to marry him.
- They will get married.

Award 1 mark for a reasonable explanation to support this prediction. For example:
- because the prince knows that she is a real princess and he has been waiting a long time to find one to share his castle with

Test 3 (page 8)

1 **Award 1 mark for all four correct:**

A man on a magic carpet flies into the classroom.	2
Mr Potter notices the man.	4
The window opens by itself.	1
The carpet lands on the floor with a bump.	3

2 Monday   **1 mark**

3 He is busy trying to mend the doors.   **1 mark**

4 He is surprised/shocked/confused/lost for words.   **1 mark**

5 **Award 2 marks for three correct or 1 mark for two correct:**
- He is quite old.
- He has a pointed beard.
- He has bright eyes.
- He is wearing glasses.
- He is wet from the rain.
- He looks ordinary.

Test 4 (page 10)

1 Somalia   **1 mark**

2 shivered   **1 mark**

3 **Award 1 mark for all three correct:**
his name (Hassan), hello and toilet

4 He didn't know what to do.   **1 mark**

5 **Award 2 marks for two correct or 1 mark for one correct:**
- He doesn't feel at home.
- He only understands three words.
- He doesn't know what the food is.
- He doesn't know how to paint (the implication being that he hasn't been in an English classroom before).
- He isn't used to the cold weather.

Test 5 (page 12)

1 wet   **1 mark**

2 **Award 1 mark for all four correct:**
cold, windy, wet and snow

3 the alphabet   **1 mark**

4 worried   **1 mark**

5 the weatherman   **1 mark**

6 **Award 1 mark for an answer that demonstrates an understanding that they want to go out to play only when it is time for lessons again.**

Answers

Test 6 (page 14)

1 cider   **1 mark**

2 He saved their lives.   **1 mark**

3 ravenous   **1 mark**

4 **Award 1 mark for all three lines drawn correctly:**

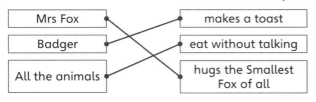

5 happy   **1 mark**

Award 1 mark for an explanation that acknowledges the positive, celebratory tone of the text or quotes a suitable extract. For example:

- The animals are celebrating.
- The animals are having a feast.
- They are happy that Mr Fox has saved them.
- They hug each other.
- They toast Mr Fox.
- 'amid shouts of joy'
- 'everyone clapped and cheered'

Test 7 (page 16)

1 **Award 1 mark for both correct:**
whispered and murmured

2 **Award 1 mark for a sensible suggestion.**
For example:
- because she has to say goodbye to Sky
- because she cannot keep Sky
- because her mum and dad say that Sky deserves a better home

3 quickly   **1 mark**

4 because she has never been upstairs and wonders what it will be like   **1 mark**

5 She purred excitedly.   **1 mark**

6 **Award 1 mark for both correct:**
- sit on the windowsill
- snooze on the duvet

Test 8 (page 18)

1 children   **1 mark**

2 Head teacher (of Little Piper Primary School)   **1 mark**

3 **Award 1 mark for all three correct:**
- Stress levels would be reduced.
- Everyone in school would feel happier.
- It would teach pupils about responsibility.

4 **Award 1 mark for all three correct:**
hospitals, care homes and schools

5 **Award 1 mark for each correct reason, up to a maximum of 2 marks:**

Animal	Reason
Cat	It could catch mice (in the store cupboard).
Sheep	It would eat the grass. or It would save money as a gardener would no longer be needed.

Test 9 (page 20)

1 The moon shone brightly.   **1 mark**

2 pebbles   **1 mark**

3 to collect pebbles   **1 mark**

4 quarrel   **1 mark**

5 **Award 1 mark for each correct answer, up to a maximum of 2 marks:**
- She calls them 'lazy bones'.
- She gives them only one piece of bread each and says they will not get any more.
- The way she speaks to them is not very nice.
- She makes them collect wood for her.

Test 10 (page 22)

1 wet ('never-ending rain')   **1 mark**

2 cantering   **1 mark**

3 She is surprised.   **1 mark**

4 **Award 1 mark for all three lines drawn correctly:**

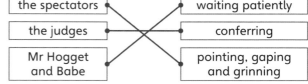

5 disappear **1 mark**

6 **Award 1 mark for one of the following:**
- The judges will allow Mr Hogget and Babe to compete.
- The sheep will disappear (when they see Babe).
- Everyone will have a good laugh.

Test 11 (page 24)

1 cloudy and chilly **1 mark**

2 wandered and strolled **1 mark**

3 no-one/They go on their own. **1 mark**

4 go on a boat ride **1 mark**

5 **Award 1 mark for acknowledging a positive emotion (various answers possible).** For example:
- They are happy.
- They enjoy it.

Award 1 mark for an appropriate piece of supporting evidence. For example:
- They 'felt so pleased to be there'.
- They say, 'it felt like an escape'.

Test 12 (page 26)

1 sea lions and an iguana
(Also accept fish.) **1 mark**

2 **Award 2 marks for all four correct or 1 mark for two or three correct:**

Sentence	True	False
Nim is left alone on the island for three days and three nights.	✓	
Nim whistles her shell three times.		✓
Nim has three cords around her neck.	✓	
Nim picks three coconuts from the tree.		✓

3 scuttling or twined **1 mark**

4 because he is hungry **1 mark**

5 spiky **1 mark**

Test 13 (page 28)

1 Italy/Lake Garda/Venice **1 mark**

2 a swimming pool and a disco **1 mark**

3 gondola **1 mark**

4 **Award 2 marks for all four correct or 1 mark for two or three correct:**

Sentence	True	False
Mia is writing to her pen pal.		✓
The flight was three hours long.	✓	
The hotel did not have a swimming pool.		✓
There are no roads for cars in Venice.	✓	

5 **Award 1 mark for an appropriate explanation.** For example:
- She says, "I loved being on the plane!"
- She loved being on the plane but thought the airport was a bit boring.

Test 14 (page 30)

1 because they are hot **1 mark**

2 because a beetle crawls out from it **1 mark**

3 **Award 2 marks for all five lines drawn correctly and 1 mark for three lines drawn correctly:**

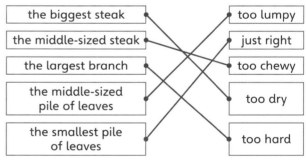

4 made such a mess **1 mark**

5 **Award 1 mark for reference to at least one of the following pieces of evidence from the text:**
- She is woken suddenly by the roaring.
- She gasps in horror.
- She leaps from the tree.
- She runs away (never to return again).

Answers

Test 15 (page 32)

1. monkeys and dogs — **1 mark**
2. to rescue the people who were on board — **1 mark**
3. citizen — **1 mark**
4. the city's port — **1 mark**
5. **Award 1 mark for each correct answer, up to a maximum of 2 marks:**
   - The monkey says Piraeus is his best friend, but really it is a port.
   - The dolphin turns its head and sees that it is a monkey.

Test 16 (page 34)

1. paper — **1 mark**
2. Accept any two from: bangs, crackles, popping, explode. — **1 mark**
3. **Award 2 marks for all four correct or 1 mark for two or three correct:**

Sentence	True	False
Most fireworks are made in China.	✓	
Fireworks are only used on Bonfire Night.		✓
Fireworks were invented in England.		✓
Fireworks are not very noisy.		✓

4. at a wedding (of Henry VII) — **1 mark**
5. dangerous — **1 mark**

Test 17 (page 36)

1. chomping — **1 mark**
2. **Award 1 mark for one of the following:**
   - He doesn't understand where it is coming from.
   - He thinks, "Weird or what?"
3. (a coat of rank and) rotten onions — **1 mark**
4. He realises that his dad isn't scared. — **1 mark**
5. **Award 1 mark for each plausible reason, up to a maximum of 2 marks (various answers possible).** For example:
   - He isn't frightened.
   - He is offended by what the voice has said.
   - He wants to protect his cub.
   - He wants to scare the man away.

Test 18 (page 38)

1. a net — **1 mark**
2. Gaffer — **1 mark**
3. lolloped — **1 mark**
4. **Award 1 mark for one of the following:**
   - because the otters have knocked on the door
   - because he is not expecting to see otters at the door
5. **Award 1 mark for both correct:**
   - He isn't eating.
   - He looks very ill.
6. The men might want to fatten him for his coat. — **1 mark**

Test 19 (page 40)

1. a poem — **1 mark**
2. a fly — **1 mark**
3. **Award 2 marks for all five correct or 1 mark for three correct:**

rosebud	golden wire
hair	coals of fire
mustard-seed	cruel leopard
loaf of bread	lofty hill
wasp	feather bed

4. a rose(bud) — **1 mark**
5. cruel — **1 mark**

Test 20 (page 42)

1. **Award 1 mark for any two of the following:**
   - coffee filter paper
   - hole punch/sharp pencil
   - felt tips/colouring pencils
   - paper straw
   - sticky tape
   - cardboard tube/toilet roll
   - mirrored card
2. to create colourful patterns — **1 mark**

3 putting a hole in the filter paper **1 mark**

4 Award 1 mark for all four correct:

Attach the straw to the tube.	4
Fold the mirrored card.	5
Put a straw through the filter paper.	3
Make a hole in the filter paper.	2
Decorate the filter paper.	1

5 flexible **1 mark**

6 Award 1 mark for an answer that includes some reference both to it being a set of instructions *and* to the kaleidoscope. For example:
- How to make a kaleidoscope
- Instructions for making a kaleidoscope
- Steps for making a kaleidoscope

Test **21** (page 44)

1 Award 1 mark for all three correct:

Sentence	True	False
Otters have short legs and long tails.	✓	
All otters live in rivers.		✓
The number of otters is going up in all areas of the country.	✓	

2 Award 2 marks for all three correct or 1 mark for one correct:

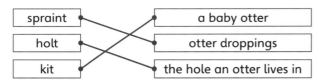

spraint	a baby otter
holt	otter droppings
kit	the hole an otter lives in

3 fish **1 mark**

4 predator(s) **1 mark**

5 Award 1 mark for both correct:
footprints and droppings (or spraints)

Test **22** (page 46)

1 the South Pole/the Antarctic/Antarctica **1 mark**

2 Award 1 mark for one of the following:
- because he made many important scientific discoveries
- because he set a record by getting closer to the South Pole than anyone had done before

3 Award 1 mark for all three correct:

Endurance	3
Discovery	1
Nimrod	2

4 Award 2 marks for all four correct or 1 mark for two or three correct:

Sentence	True	False
Shackleton was born in London.		✓
Shackleton's father wanted him to become a doctor.	✓	
Shackleton went on three expeditions.	✓	
Shackleton was the first explorer to reach the South Pole.		✓

5 because they escaped on smaller boats **1 mark**

This book of answers is a pull-out section from **KS1 SATs Reading 10-Minute Tests**.

Published by **Schofield & Sims Ltd**, 7 Mariner Court, Wakefield, West Yorkshire WF4 3FL, UK
Telephone 01484 607080
www.schofieldandsims.co.uk

This edition copyright © Schofield & Sims Ltd, 2019
First published in 2019
Second impression 2020

Author: **Rachel Lopiccolo**

British Library Cataloguing in Publication Data
A catalogue record for this book is available from the British Library.

Design by **Ledgard Jepson**
Printed in the UK by **Page Bros (Norwich) Ltd**

ISBN 978 07217 1498 1

1   What is the weather like on the day the poet visits York? Tick **two**.

sunny ☐   raining ☐   cloudy ☐   chilly ☐   ☐

1 mark

2   **Find** and **copy two** words that the poet uses instead of *walked*.

1) ....

2) ....   ☐

1 mark

3   Who does the poet go to York with?

....   ☐

1 mark

4   Which of the following things does the poet **not** do? Tick **one**.

go on a train ☐   go on a boat ride ☐

have a coffee ☐   walk by the river ☐   ☐

1 mark

5   How does the poet feel about their day in York?

....

How can you tell?

....

....

....   ☐

2 marks

Total marks ....   Time taken ....

Test **12**

Extract from *Nim's Island* by Wendy Orr

In a palm tree, on an island, in the middle of the wide blue sea, was a girl.

Nim's hair was wild, her eyes were bright, and round her neck she wore three cords. One was for a spyglass, one was for a whirly, whistling shell, and the other a fat, red pocket-knife in a sheath.

With the spyglass at her eye, she watched her father's boat. It sailed out through the reef to the darker, deeper ocean, and Jack turned to wave and Nim waved back, though she knew he couldn't see.

Then the white sails caught the wind and blew him out of sight, and Nim was alone. For three days and three nights, whatever happened or needed doing, Nim would do it.

"And what we need first," said Nim, "is breakfast." So she threw four ripe coconuts *thump!* into the sand and climbed down after them.

Then she whistled her shell, two long, shrill notes that carried far out to the reef where the sea lions were fishing. Selkie popped her head above the water. She had a fish in her mouth, but she swallowed it fast and dived towards the beach.

And from a rock by the hut, Fred came scuttling. Fred was an iguana, spiky as a dragon, with a cheerful snub nose. He twined around Nim's feet in a prickly hug.

"Are you saying good morning," Nim demanded, "or just begging for breakfast?"

Fred stared at the coconuts. He was a very honest iguana.

spyglass = a small telescope

1 Which **two** types of animal are mentioned in the story?

1) ....

2) ....

1 mark

2 Put ticks in the table to show which sentences are **true** and which are **false**.

Sentence	True	False
Nim is left alone on the island for three days and three nights.		
Nim whistles her shell three times.		
Nim has three cords around her neck.		
Nim picks three coconuts from the tree.		

2 marks

3 Find and **copy one** word that describes how Fred moves.

....

1 mark

4 Why does Fred stare at the coconuts? Tick **one**.

because he wants to play with Nim ☐

because he is saying good morning ☐

because he is hungry ☐

because he has never seen one before ☐

1 mark

5 **Find** and **copy one** word that means the same as *prickly*.

....

1 mark

Total marks ....   Time taken ....

Test 13

Dear Diary,

I'm sorry that I haven't written for the last 10 days but I have been on the most amazing holiday and I forgot to take you with me. Let me tell you all about it.

On Monday last week, we had to get up at 4 o'clock in the morning to get a taxi to the airport. The airport was sort of exciting but also boring at the same time. We had to queue up to show our tickets, have our bags sent down a moving track and have our passports checked. There were some shops and restaurants but Dad said we had to sit and watch the planes out of the window. I complained, but it was actually quite cool.

I loved being on the plane! I sat next to the window and we could see all of Manchester as we took off. When we landed, three hours later, we got off the plane and walked along the runway – it was so hot!

Italy was amazing. We got a bus from Verona airport to Lake Garda and stayed in a hotel with the biggest pool I've ever seen. There was a disco every night and sometimes a singer. One day we went to Venice and got to go in a gondola along the canals. They don't have roads for cars in Venice – just narrow streets full of people and canals full of boats!

It was a brilliant holiday but now I'm back to the Lancashire rain, wishing I was in Italy again.

Back to school tomorrow.

Mia

---

1 Where did Mia spend her holiday?

....

1 mark

---

2 What does Mia say was at the hotel? Tick **two**.

a swimming pool ☐   a cinema ☐

a restaurant ☐   a disco ☐

1 mark

---

3 **Find** and **copy one** word for the type of boat Mia travelled on in Venice.

....

1 mark

---

4 Put ticks in the table to show which sentences are **true** and which are **false**.

Sentence	True	False
Mia is writing to her pen pal.		
The flight was three hours long.		
The hotel did not have a swimming pool.		
There are no roads for cars in Venice.		

2 marks

---

5 How can you tell that Mia preferred being on the plane to being at the airport?

....

....

1 mark

Total marks ....   Time taken ....

Test 14

'Neema and the Three Lions'

Once upon a time, there lived a family of lions. One morning, the weather was too hot for them to eat their breakfast steaks, so they went out for a refreshing drink of water.

While they were gone, a young girl called Neema came across the lions' den. She took one look at the steaks and couldn't resist them. First, she took a bite from the biggest steak, but it was too dry. Next, she took a bite from the middle-sized steak, but it was too chewy. Then she took a bite from the smallest steak and it was just right. So she ate every last bit.

Neema was tired from her walk and spotted three piles of leaves in the corner of the den. She flopped onto the largest pile, but it was too squishy. She tried the middle-sized pile, but it was too lumpy. She tried the smallest pile and it was just right, but as she was settling down a beetle crawled out and started running around the floor.

Neema looked for somewhere else to rest. She climbed up a nearby tree and lay on the largest branch, but it was too hard. She moved to the middle-sized branch, but it was too spiky. Finally, she moved to the smallest branch and it was just right. Neema fell fast asleep.

She was so busy snoring and dreaming of steak that she did not notice when the lion family returned.

Papa and Mama roared, "Who has been eating my steak?"

Then Baby cried, "Who has been eating my steak? They've eaten it all!"

Then Papa saw that the piles of leaves were not as they had left them.

"Who has been sitting on my leaves?" Papa and Mama roared together.

"And who has been sitting on my leaves? They've made such a mess!" Baby cried.

Then the lions looked up into the tree.

Papa and Mama roared, "Who has been sleeping on my branch?"

Baby cried, "Who has been sleeping on my branch? They're still there!"

The three lions roared together and Neema woke up suddenly. She gasped in horror, leapt out of the tree and ran, never to return again.

1 Why do the lions leave their den at the beginning of the story?
Tick **one**.

because it is morning ☐   because they are hungry ☐

because they are hot ☐   because they are cold ☐   ☐

1 mark

2 Why does Neema not stay on the smallest pile of leaves?

....   ☐

1 mark

3 Draw **five** lines to match the object to what Neema thinks about it.

the biggest steak •	• too lumpy
the middle-sized steak •	• just right
the largest branch •	• too chewy
the middle-sized pile of leaves •	• too dry
the smallest pile of leaves •	• too hard

☐

2 marks

4 What does Baby say someone has done to his pile of leaves?

....   ☐

1 mark

5 Look again at the last paragraph. How do we know that Neema
feels scared? Explain your answer using evidence from the text.

....

....   ☐

1 mark

Total marks ....   Time taken ....

Test 15

'The Monkey and the Dolphin', a fable by Aesop

One stormy day many years ago, a Greek ship headed for Athens was wrecked near the city's port, Piraeus. At that time, the dolphins thought very highly of people, especially the Athenians, so they swam to the wreck to rescue the people who had fallen into the sea.

One dolphin saw what he thought was a man and went to his rescue. However, as well as people, the ship had been carrying monkeys and dogs. The dolphin did not realise that what he had thought was a man was in fact a monkey.

"Climb upon my back, young sir, and let me take you to shore," the dolphin called as it swam towards the monkey.

The monkey sat upon the dolphin's back, grateful to be rescued.

"You must be a citizen of Athens," the dolphin uttered gently.

"Oh yes," replied the monkey, "I am from a noble family."

"Wow," sighed the dolphin, feeling humbled to have rescued such an important Athenian. "So you must visit Piraeus often."

"Oh, yes! I see him all the time. He is my best friend."

The dolphin was surprised and shocked at the reply. He turned his head and saw that he was not in fact carrying a noble Athenian but a lowly monkey. The dolphin dived away, leaving the foolish monkey to find his own way back to shore.

Athenian = a person from Athens
lowly = low in importance

1   Which **two** types of animal are aboard the ship?

1) ....

2) ....

1 mark

---

2   Why does the dolphin go to where the ship is wrecked?

....

1 mark

---

3   **Find** and **copy one** word that means someone who lives in a particular town or city.

....

1 mark

---

4   What is Piraeus? Tick **one**.

a Greek ship ☐   the dolphin's name ☐

the city's port ☐   a noble man from Athens ☐

☐

1 mark

---

5   What makes the dolphin realise that he has been tricked? Mention **two** things.

1) ....

....

2) ....

....

2 marks

Total marks ....   Time taken ....

Test 16

How do Fireworks Work?

Fireworks are used not only on Bonfire Night but also for celebrations throughout the year, such as New Year's Eve, weddings and other special events.

They light up the sky with spectacular colours and create big bangs and crackles that can be heard miles away.

But how do they actually work?

Every firework contains a shell, usually made of heavy paper. Inside the shell, there is a substance called gunpowder, which can burn really fast.

When someone wants to set off a firework, they light a piece of string called the fuse, which then sets fire to the gunpowder. The fuse continues to burn as the firework shoots up into the sky, until the spark reaches the shell.

The gunpowder then burns up quickly, creating popping sounds. Salts which are packed into the shell then explode to make different colours and sparkles that light up the sky. If these salts are placed in different sections within the shell, they will explode at different times, creating different patterns.

Did you know?

- Fireworks were invented in China over 2,000 years ago.
- Nearly all fireworks sold around the world today are made in China.
- The first known use of fireworks in England was at the wedding of Henry VII in 1486.
- Fireworks are very dangerous – they should never be used by children.

Henry VII = a king of England

1 What is the shell inside a firework usually made of? Tick **one**.

paper ☐ wood ☐ glass ☐ metal ☐

☐
1 mark

2 **Find** and **copy two** sounds that fireworks make.

1) ....

2) ....

☐
1 mark

3 Put ticks in the table to show which sentences are **true** and which are **false**.

Sentence	True	False
Most fireworks are made in China.		
Fireworks are only used on Bonfire Night.		
Fireworks were invented in England.		
Fireworks are not very noisy.		

☐
2 marks

4 At what type of event were fireworks first used in England?

....

☐
1 mark

5 **Find** and **copy one** word that means the same as *unsafe*.

....

☐
1 mark

Total marks .... Time taken ....

Extract from *The Fox and the Ghost King* by Michael Morpurgo

It is night time. A fox cub and his father are out hunting near Leicester City Football Club. They hear a strange voice.

I was happily chomping away on the nice fat wriggly worm I had just caught, which was trying to curl itself round my nose, when I thought I heard a strange voice. It seemed close by and yet far away at the same time. And somehow it was coming from below me too.

Weird or what? I thought.

Dad had heard it as well. His ears were pricked, turning, turning, this way and that, and that way and this.

Then the voice spoke again, definitely a man's voice, and it really was coming from somewhere deep below the ground.

"I know a fox when I smell one," it said. "You all wear your smell about you like a coat of rank and rotten onions."

I could feel the hair standing up in fear all along the back of my neck. But Dad wasn't frightened, so after a moment or two I wasn't either. Like me, he was looking for the voice, trying to smell and hear exactly where it might be coming from. So I did the same.

Dad spoke then, in his growliest, angriest voice: "I don't know who you are, but how we smell is our business. So, whoever and wherever you are, you have no business making rude remarks to strangers you have never met, and who mean you no harm and have never hurt you."

rank = very smelly

1 **Find** and **copy one** word that means the same as eating.

chopp ~~chopp~~ chomping

1 mark

2 How can you tell that the young fox is confused when he first hears the voice?

I heard a strange ⚡voice

1 mark

3 What does the voice say foxes smell like?

rank and roton onionce

1 mark

4 What makes the young fox stop being scared of the voice?

Tick **one**.

He works out who it is. ☐

He realises that his dad isn't scared. ☑

He works out where the voice is coming from. ☐

His dad speaks to the voice. ☐

1 mark

5 Why do you think Dad speaks in his *growliest, angriest voice*?

Mention **two** reasons.

1) so what or who gets scaored

2) to sound feathes

2 marks

Total marks _____ Time taken _____

Test 18

Extract from *The Otter Who Wanted to Know* by Jill Tomlinson

Pat and Bobby are otters who were frightened away from their home by a shark. They were taken in by men who fed them and then released them. They are near the men's hut, watching what is going on.

Later they saw Fishface go off with one of the nets. When he came back he had another otter in it. Pat stood up, her eyes bright, her whiskers quivering. "Who is it?" she asked. "Is it someone we know? Do you think it's Gaffer?"

She and Bobby watched the man go into the warm hut.

"I am going to see who it is," Bobby said. "You stay here while I find out." But of course Pat followed him to the hut.

They banged on the door with their paws, and Whitehair (that's what they called him) opened it, with a look of surprise on his face. They just lolloped past him, straight to the bath.

It wasn't Gaffer. It was Dud, the young otter, looking very ill indeed. He was even refusing the fish he had been offered. He had never been known to refuse food in his life.

"Come on, Dud," said Bobby. "Eat up. They're nice men, and they'll soon have you well."

"You're sure they're not just fattening us for our coats?" asked Dud.

1 What does Fishface use to catch the otter?

....

1 mark

2 Who does Pat think Fishface has caught?

....

1 mark

3 Look at the paragraph starting *They banged on the door...*
Find and **copy one** word that describes how the otters move.

....

1 mark

4 Why do you think Whitehair is surprised when he opens the door?

....

1 mark

5 How do the otters know that Dud is not very well? Tick **two**.

He isn't eating. ☐   He is with the men. ☐

He is in a bath. ☐   He looks very ill. ☐

1 mark

6 What is Dud worried about? Tick **one**.

The food doesn't look nice. ☐

The men might want to fatten him for his coat. ☐

He doesn't know where Gaffer is. ☐

He doesn't like being in the bath. ☐

1 mark

Total marks ....   Time taken ....

'The Fly'

How large unto the tiny fly
Must little things appear –
A rosebud like a feather bed,
Its prickle like a spear;
A dewdrop like a looking-glass,
A hair like golden wire;
The smallest grain of mustard-seed
As fierce as coals of fire;
A loaf of bread, a lofty hill;
A wasp, a cruel leopard;
And specks of salt as bright to see
As lambkins to a shepherd.

Walter Ramal

unto = to
looking-glass = mirror
lofty = high
lambkins = lambs

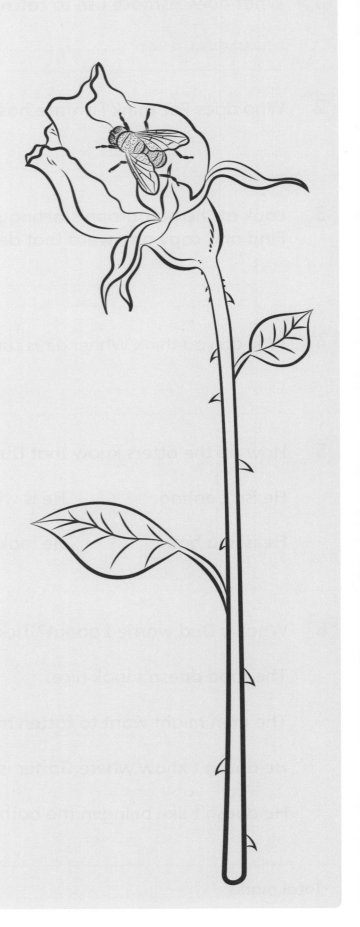

1 What sort of writing is this? Tick **one**.

an adventure story ☐   a poem ☐

an explanation text ☐   a traditional tale ☐

☐
1 mark

2 What type of creature is the writing about?

....

☐
1 mark

3 Draw **five** lines to match the object to its description.

rosebud	•	•	golden wire
hair	•	•	coals of fire
mustard-seed	•	•	cruel leopard
loaf of bread	•	•	lofty hill
wasp	•	•	feather bed

☐
2 marks

4 What is described as having a *prickle like a spear*?

....

☐
1 mark

5 **Find** and **copy one** word that means the same as *unkind*.

....

☐
1 mark

Total marks ....   Time taken ....

Test **20**

Kaleidoscopes use colours and mirrors to create beautiful patterns as they are turned. By following these instructions, you can create your very own amazing kaleidoscope.

You will need:

- coffee filter paper
- a hole punch or sharp pencil
- felt tips or colouring pencils
- a paper straw
- sticky tape
- a cardboard tube – from a toilet roll, for example
- mirrored card that is flexible enough to be folded.

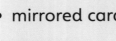

Instructions

First, decorate your coffee filter paper using the coloured pens or pencils. You will get the best effect if you divide the paper into three or four sections and create a different pattern in each one – the more colourful the better!

Next, put a hole in the middle of the decorated filter paper. You might need an adult to help you with this part. You could use a hole punch or poke a hole through with a sharp pencil.

Push the straw through the hole in the filter paper and secure it in place with a piece of sticky tape. The plain side of the filter paper should be the side with the sticky tape on it.

Stick the straw to the side of the tube using sticky tape so that the filter paper is against one end of the tube. The decorated side should be against the tube.

Now, fold your mirrored card into three equal parts so that it fits inside your tube to form a triangular prism shape, and slide it into the tube.

Hold your kaleidoscope up to the light and slowly turn the filter paper. You should be treated to a wonderful display of colour and shape!

1 Name **two** things that you need to make a kaleidoscope.

1) ....

2) ....

1 mark

2 What is the purpose of a kaleidoscope? Tick **one**.

to help you see things more clearly ☐

to create colourful patterns ☐

to make coffee with ☐

to decorate your window ☐

☐
1 mark

3 What does the text say you might need an adult's help with?

☐
1 mark

....

4 Number these instructions from 1 to 5 to show the order in which you would do them. The first one has been done for you.

Attach the straw to the tube.	
Fold the mirrored card.	
Put a straw through the filter paper.	
Make a hole in the filter paper.	
Decorate the filter paper.	1

☐
1 mark

5 Look at the section called **You will need**.
Find and **copy one** word that means the same as *bendy*.

☐
1 mark

....

6 The text does not yet have a title. Write a suitable title.

☐
1 mark

....

Total marks .... Time taken ....

All About Otters

Otters are part of the weasel family, which also includes badgers. They live near water and their bodies are designed to help them to swim and turn quickly in the water. They have short legs, long tails and very flexible bodies. Most otters live near rivers, but sea otters have adapted to live in coastal areas.

What do otters eat?

Otters are predators. This means that they hunt other animals for food. They live mainly on a diet of fish, such as eels, which they catch while swimming. Sometimes they also catch and eat frogs, ducks, crabs and small mammals.

Where do otters live?

Otters live along river banks in holes called holts. They prefer to use empty rabbit warrens or holes created by tree roots, rather than dig their own. They usually live alone, but will live in family groups when the females have their babies, which are called kits. Kits live with their mother for up to one year.

Otters are very shy creatures and are rarely seen. However, otter footprints in the mud along the edge of rivers are a clue that otters are nearby. Otter footprints look similar to those of a small dog. Spraints, or otter droppings, are also evidence of otters. Spraints include lots of small fish bones.

What does the future hold for otters?

The number of otters in the UK was falling until recently because they were hunted for their fur and they suffered from the presence of pollution in rivers. However, otters are now protected, and the number of them is increasing in all areas of the country.

1 Put ticks in the table to show which sentences are **true** and which are **false**.

Sentence	True	False
Otters have short legs and long tails.		
All otters live in rivers.		
The number of otters is going up in all areas of the country.		

1 mark

2 Draw **three** lines to match the words to their meanings. Look at how the words are used in the text to help you.

spraints			a baby otter

| holt | | | otter droppings |

| kit | | | the hole an otter lives in |

2 marks

3 What do otters mostly eat? Tick **one**.

crabs ☐   frogs ☐   weasels ☐   fish ☐

1 mark

4 Look at the section called **What do otters eat? Find** and **copy one** word that means that otters hunt and eat other animals.

....

1 mark

5 What **two** things are clues that an otter may be nearby?

1) ....

2) ....

1 mark

Total marks ....   Time taken ....

Test 22

Ernest Shackleton

Ernest Shackleton was born in 1874 in Ireland, but he and his family moved to London while Ernest was a young child. His father wanted him to become a doctor, but instead Ernest joined the merchant navy. He travelled widely and had a passion for adventure.

In 1901, Shackleton was chosen to go on an expedition to the Antarctic led by Robert Falcon Scott on the ship *Discovery*. Shackleton went towards the South Pole in difficult conditions, and managed to get closer to the South Pole than anyone had been before. But, while he was there, Shackleton became very ill and had to return home.

In 1908, Shackleton led his own expedition to the South Pole on the ship *Nimrod*. During the expedition, he made many important scientific discoveries and set a record by getting even closer to the South Pole than before. He received a reward from the king when he returned to Britain.

In 1914, Shackleton made his third trip to the Antarctic with the ship *Endurance*, planning to cross Antarctica via the South Pole. By this time, two other explorers had already reached the South Pole, meaning Shackleton could no longer be the first. However, early in 1915, *Endurance* became trapped in the ice and 10 months later she sank. Luckily, no members of the expedition died because they escaped on smaller boats.

Shackleton planned another expedition to Antarctica, but on 5th January 1922 he died of a heart attack without having achieved his goal.

expedition = a journey to a place to find out more about it

---

1   Where did Shackleton go on his expeditions?

....

1 mark

---

2   Why do you think Shackleton received a reward from the king?

....

1 mark

---

3 Number the ships from 1 to 3 to show the order in which Shackleton sailed on them.

Endurance	
Discovery	
Nimrod	

1 mark

4 Put ticks in the table to show which sentences are **true** and which are **false**.

Sentence	True	False
Shackleton was born in London.		
Shackleton's father wanted him to become a doctor.		
Shackleton went on three expeditions.		
Shackleton was the first explorer to reach the South Pole.		

2 marks

5 Why did no-one die when the ship *Endurance* sank?

Tick **one**.

because the water wasn't very cold ☐

because it had been trapped for 10 months ☐

because they escaped on smaller boats ☐

because two other explorers had reached the South Pole ☐

1 mark

Total marks .... Time taken ....

Progress chart

Write the score (out of 6) for each test in the box provided to the right of the chart. Then colour the row next to the box to represent this score.

	1	2	3	4	5	6	Total
Test 1							
Test 2							
Test 3							
Test 4							
Test 5							
Test 6							
Test 7							
Test 8							
Test 9							
Test 10							
Test 11							
Test 12							
Test 13							
Test 14							
Test 15							
Test 16							
Test 17							
Test 18							
Test 19							
Test 20							
Test 21							
Test 22							

Score (out of 6)